Retirement
FOR
DUMMIES®

Compliments of
REAL *Powered by* Humana

WILEY

Wiley Publishing, Inc.

Retirement For Dummies®

Published by Wiley Publishing, Inc.
111 River St.
Hoboken, NJ 07030-5774
www.wiley.com

Copyright © 2009 by Wiley Publishing, Inc., Indianapolis, Indiana

Published simultaneously in Canada

For general information on our other products and services, please contact our Customer Care Department within the U.S. at 800-762-2974, outside the U.S. at 317-572-3993, or fax 317-572-4002.

For technical support, please visit www.wiley.com/techsupport.

Wiley also publishes its books in a variety of electronic formats. Some content that appears in print may not be available in electronic books.

ISBN: 978-0-470-43884-8

Manufactured in the United States of America

10 9 8 7 6 5 4 3 2 1

WILEY

Publisher's Acknowledgments

Project Editor: Elizabeth Kuball

Composition Services: Indianapolis Composition Services Department

Cover Photo: © iStock.com

Table of Contents

Introduction *1*

    About This Book 1
    Icons Used in This Book...................................1
    Where to Go from Here 2

Chapter 1: Getting Your Body Fit and Healthy *3*

    Raising Your Expectations: Preparing for a Longer Life 3
    Understanding the Benefits of Being Fit 4
    Sizing Up Your Fitness Level................................5
    Exercising for Life 8
    Seeking a Mind-Body Connection 12

Chapter 2: The ABCs (and D) of Medicare *15*

    Knowing When You Qualify 15
    Examining Costs and Coverage in Medicare's Four Parts ...17
    Getting with the Program: When and How to Sign Up for
        Parts A and B 20
    Lowering Costs and Adding Benefits.....................24
    Finding Out More about Medicare.........................26

Chapter 3: Caring for Your Loved Ones
(Including Yourself!) *27*

    Parenting Skills That Span Generations 28
    Recognizing the Challenges of Aging....................31
    Coping with Caregiver Burnout.............................34

Chapter 4: Managing Your Retirement Savings
So You Don't Run Out.......................................*39*

    Investing the Money You Have..............................39
    Taking Out Your Money: The Official Rules............42
    Making Sure Your Savings Lasts as Long as You Do.............45
    Determining Your Budget....................................47
    Calculating Whether Your Income Is Enough.......................51
    Making That Critical Decision: Stay Retired
        or Go Back to Work? 52

Chapter 5: Finally, 1 Can Relax! Planning to Travel 57

Indulging in Adventure: Alaska 53
Australia: Enjoying the Trip of a Lifetime 56
Fun for All Generations: The Yucatán 58
Plan Your Own Destination Vacation......................................60
On the Road Again: Seeing the USA..61
Enjoying a Volunteer Vacation...64
Booking Your Trip, Saving Money, and Staying Safe............65

Introduction

*A*s you approach retirement, life can bring a new set of challenges, leaving you with lots of unanswered questions. What's the best workout now that you're over 40? How do you make the most of your retirement savings — and make it last? How do you keep up with your grandchildren? Have better relationships with your grown children? Take care of your aging parents? Can you finally plan that trip you've always dreamed of?

In this book, REAL *Powered by* Humana helps you get answers to these challenges by covering the topics that matter to you. Focused on physical fitness, understanding Medicare, caring for loved ones, managing retirement savings, and travel, each chapter includes helpful tips and expert advice and is easy to understand. And it's all part of a clear-cut program you can use to plan retirement step by step.

About This Book

Retirement For Dummies is all about empowering you to sail the uncharted waters ahead. It's divided into five chapters that you can read in succession, like a good novel, or dip into to find answers to the questions you have right now. Either way, you'll gain the knowledge you need to head into your retirement years with confidence.

Icons Used in This Book

We use icons in the margins throughout this book to draw your attention to points that are especially valuable or important. Here's what each icon means:

When we tell you something that could save you time or money or just make your life a little easier, we mark it with this icon.

You don't have to commit this book to memory any more than you have to memorize the dictionary to make use of it. But when we tell you something that's so important that you really *should* remember it, we flag it with this icon.

Life is full of pitfalls and quicksand, but you don't have to fall in — if you heed the warnings marked with this icon, you can sidestep the problems.

Odds are, kids are a part of your life — in the form of your own little ones or your grandchildren (or both!). In Chapter 5, the chapter on travel, when we tell you about a place that's especially great for kids, we mark it with this icon.

Sometimes we get so into a particular subject that we can't *help* but share the technical details. When that happens, we flag it with a Technical Stuff icon. If you're as engrossed as we are in the subject, you'll enjoy reading these paragraphs — but if you're in a hurry and just want the information you absolutely need, you can safely skip anything marked with this icon.

Where to Go from Here

If you've gone from high school to college to work to marriage to kids, you're probably used to doing what's "supposed to be" next. Retirement is your chance to shake things up, and it starts with this book. Rule number one: There are no rules! You can read this book in any order you want. If you're planning the trip of a lifetime, make Chapter 5 your destination. If you're trying to figure out if you have enough money to retire, Chapter 4 is for you. Maybe you're trying to make sense of that big puzzle called Medicare — if so, start with Chapter 2. You can read the chapters in any order you want and still get to the same destination: knowledge and power to face whatever challenges lie ahead.

Visit www.RealForMe.com for more information, expert advice, and tools that delve deeper into the topics covered in this book, or to participate in discussions and learn about other issues that are important to you.

Chapter 1

Getting Your Body Fit and Healthy

● ●

In This Chapter

▶ Tallying up the benefits of being physically fit

▶ Assessing your own fitness level

▶ Figuring out what to do, how often, and for how long

▶ Harnessing the power of the mind-body fitness connection

● ●

Aging is inevitable, but you don't have to shuffle into old age as a hunchback with a cane, looking for the nearest park bench to sit down on. You can feel 10, 15, even 20 years younger than the birth date on your driver's license. And if you take charge of your fitness today, you'll not only increase your chances of living longer, but you'll improve your quality of life. When you're healthy, you're able to travel, care for loved ones, give back to your community, spend time with your family and friends . . . the list is endless.

Don't worry if you haven't exactly been a regular exerciser your entire life — it's never too late to start. In this chapter, we show you how.

Raising Your Expectations: Preparing for a Longer Life

You don't want to grow old. Old age is for . . . old people. Old age is your back going out more than you do. Old age is running out of breath walking *down* a flight of stairs. But old age doesn't *have* to be that way, at least for a very long time. Yes, it's inevitable that you'll grow old someday, but what influences the need for getting in shape now is the fact that folks are living longer than ever before.

People living at the dawn of the 20th century lived with the strong possibility that they could be pushing up daisies when they reached 45 years of age. One hundred years later, you find yourself living in a highly technological society with breakthrough medical advancements. You've been handed 30 extra years of life on a silver platter. What you do with those years is up to you.

Understanding the Benefits of Being Fit

When you have become physically fit, you:

- ✔ Increase your chances of living a longer, healthier life
- ✔ Reduce your risk of developing high blood pressure
- ✔ Decrease feelings of depression and anxiety
- ✔ Help control your weight
- ✔ Help build and maintain healthy bones, muscles, and joints
- ✔ Become stronger and better able to perform not only the tasks you *need* to do (like cooking and cleaning and household chores) but also the activities you *want* to do (like traveling, hiking, and caring for those you love)
- ✔ Increase your energy, allowing you to do more of the things you enjoy
- ✔ Promote your psychological well-being

Regular exercise and being fit invites overall good health to visit and stay with you a long time. Your mood will improve, you'll feel better about yourself, and you'll be able to lead a longer life.

Sizing Up Your Fitness Level

When you're facing retirement and you suspect you may not be as fit as you'd like, one of the first steps you have to take is to figure out what shape you're in right now. Doing so gives you a benchmark to measure your results by. After several months on your fitness program, this reference point enables you to look back and say, "Yes, I've come a long way."

Here are several ways to determine what shape you're in:

✔ Any **fitness center** worth its mission statement can assess your fitness level. Just ask for an assessment when you sign up. A staff member measures your resting heart rate, your heart rate under physical exertion, the number of push-ups and sit-ups you can do in a minute, your strength on various exercise machines, and how long you can walk on a treadmill, among several other in-house tests.

✔ A **personal trainer,** at a gym or your house, can take the same measurements.

✔ **Self-administered tests,** like the ones we describe in the following sections, are easy to perform and take just a few minutes. These tests, though not scientific, should give you a rudimentary idea where you stand on several components of overall fitness.

Visit www.RealForMe.com for additional ways to assess your fitness level and tools to help you lead a longer, healthier life.

After you do the tests in the following sections, take a cold, hard look at the results. If you score well, treat yourself to a banana split (just kidding); seriously, congratulate yourself for being more fit than many of your peers — you probably have lots more energy for playtime with your kids or grandkids than they do. If you're out of shape, that's okay, too. Increasing your regular physical activity by even a modest amount results in measurable long-term benefits; you can find out more in the "Exercising for Life" section, later in this chapter.

Test 1: Upper body

Count how many push-ups you can do in a minute. Note your ranking. Women may do modified push-ups by starting with their knees on the ground and slightly bent.

Rankings	Number of Push-Ups
Very fit	25
Average	15
Out of shape	7
Couch potato	Fewer than 7

Test 2: Middle body

Lie down on your back. Cup your hands and place them behind your head. Do a half-sit-up and hold your body at a 45-degree angle for as long as you can. Don't forget to note your ranking.

If this exercise is a literal pain in the neck, stop immediately.

Rankings	Length of Endurance
Very fit	25 seconds
Average	15 seconds
Out of shape	7 seconds
Couch potato	Less than 7 seconds

Test 3: Lower body

Skiers should be familiar with this exercise, which is great for developing strong leg muscles. Lean against a wall and "sit" against it with your legs bent at a 90-degree right angle. Hold this position for as long as you can. (You'll feel your legs burn.) Jot down your ranking.

Rankings	Length of Endurance
Very fit	90 seconds
Average	60 seconds
Out of shape	30 seconds
Couch potato	Less than 30 seconds

Test 4: Flexibility

Before conducting this test, go for a five-minute walk and do some jumping jacks. Get loose and warm. Sit on the floor and place a yardstick between your legs so that the 15-inch mark lines up with the end of your feet (and the 1-inch mark is roughly between your knees). Your feet should be shoulder-width apart — about 10 inches. Slowly stretch forward and slide your fingertips along the yardstick as far as possible.

No sudden movements, please; you can throw your back out if you haven't done this type of stretching in a while. Reach to the point of gentle tension, never to the point of pain. Reach as far as you can at least three times, but do not bounce or bob forward with each reach.

Note: We're including info for people in their 50s here in case you're not quite to the big 6-0.

Men's Rankings	Age 50–59	Age 60–69
Very fit	16 inches or more	15 inches or more
Average	10–15 inches	9–14 inches
Out of shape	7–9 inches	6–8 inches
Couch potato	6 inches or less	5 inches or less

Women's Rankings	Age 50–59	Age 60–69
Very fit	19 inches or more	18 inches or more
Average	13–18 inches	12–17 inches
Out of shape	10–12 inches	9–11 inches
Couch potato	9 inches or less	8 inches or less

Exercising for Life

When middle-aged people think about starting to exercise again, they generally see themselves walking on a treadmill or pedaling a stationary bike — and that's it. Although aerobic exercise is important — the foundation of your exercise regimen — it is only one of three types of exercise that you should do to shape, tone, and define your body. Combining all three will give you the most complete workout possible.

You should include these three forms of exercise in your regimen: aerobic, anaerobic, and stretching. We cover all three in the following sections.

Before beginning any exercise program, check with your doctor.

The heart of it: Aerobic exercise

The body is said to be working aerobically when it operates at a pace that allows the cardio-respiratory system (the lungs, heart, and bloodstream) to replenish energy as you exercise. Put another way, *aerobic exercise* causes the body to use oxygen to create energy. This is basically anything that gets the heart going, like walking on treadmills, cycling on stationary bikes, or stepping on stair-stepper machines.

The American College of Sports Medicine recommends that aerobic activities be performed three to five times a week, for

20 to 60 minutes on each occasion. When performing aerobic exercise, you need to be aware of your maximum heart rate and target heart rate. Your maximum heart rate is 220 minus your age (so, if you're 60 years old, your maximum heart rate is 160 beats per minute).

You don't want to work out anywhere *near* your maximum heart rate, though. Instead, your target heart rate should be between 60 percent and 80 percent of your maximum. So multiply your maximum heart rate by 0.60 to find the low end of that range, and by 0.80 to find the high end of that range. (If you're 60, your range would be between 96 and 128 beats per minute.)

You can monitor your heart rate as you exercise by wearing a heart-rate monitor. Acumen (www.acumeninc.com), Polar (www.polarusa.com), and Cardiosport (www.cardio sport.com) all sell excellent models for less than $100.

The key is to find an aerobic exercise you enjoy — that way, you'll be more likely to do it regularly. Check out the following exercises, some of which you can do daily and others you may want to add in to spice things up and keep from getting bored:

- ✓ **Walking:** Walking is probably the most perfect exercise you can do and is a surprisingly effective strategy for long-term health. Walking doesn't cost a cent (unless you walk on a treadmill), can be done at any time, is not injurious, and can be as intensive as you want it to be. This load-bearing exercise places a gentle strain on the hips and the rest of the body.

- ✓ **Tennis:** Although tennis cannot be strictly considered an aerobic sport, it's a game requiring stamina, running, and strength. If you play singles with an evenly matched opponent, you'll get all the workout you want. Doubles tennis is less exercise (because you have to cover only half the court), but playing two or three sets of doubles packs plenty of exercise.

  The game builds nearly every muscle group, especially those in your legs and arms. You develop flexibility because you have to stay low and keep your knees bent when you hit forehands and backhands. Rapid twists and turns work the muscles of the lower body, including the buttocks, front of the thighs, and calf muscles. And serving is a complicated process that involves dozens of muscles in a full range of motion.

✔ **Swimming:** Water supports you, adds natural resistance that tones and strengthens the body's muscles, and works your muscles in the same way that light weights do. Water creates buoyancy that reduces the effects of gravity by 90 percent, allowing you to exercise with minimal impact on your joints. The pressure of water against your chest works your lungs and improves the body's respiratory system. Another great thing about swimming is that you don't have to be any good at it to benefit from its aerobic-inducing qualities. You can dog-paddle up and down the pool and still receive a workout that leaves you panting.

✔ **Mountain biking:** Perhaps you haven't noticed the fat-tire revolution in the world of cycling? Well, the war is over, and mountain bikes have won. In only 20 years, mountain bikes have supplanted the kinds of bikes we grew up with — three-speeds and ten-speeds — to become the most popular bike for the most popular cycling activity, mountain biking.

Mountain biking mirrors the exercise benefits found in skinny-tire cycling. You burn calories like a locomotive, strengthen the legs until they feel like anvils, and pump up your cardiovascular fitness to new heights. Mountain biking is a great way to combine physical activity with the Great Outdoors.

✔ **Rock climbing:** Rock climbing uses every muscle group in the body — not just the upper body — and increases hand-eye coordination, balance, strength, and flexibility. And you don't have to live in the mountains to do it. At indoor "rock gyms," the risks aren't nearly as great, and you're never more than 30 feet off the ground. Interestingly, rock climbing is a great equalizer between the sexes because the strength-to-weight ratio makes it easier for women to pull themselves up, especially on negative-incline walls found at most gyms.

If you're thinking, "Hey, what about golf?", we're sorry to break it to you: Golf isn't an aerobic exercise. To gain the cardiovascular benefits of walking, you need to move *continuously* for at least 20 minutes, and you really never get 20 minutes of continuous walking in golf.

The fitness heavyweight: Anaerobic exercise

Anaerobic exercise is any form of non-sustained, intense physical activity that typically involves a limited number of specific muscles over a short time, such as strength training or lifting free weights. Body-weight exercises such as sit-ups, push-ups, and pull-ups are gym-free alternatives to get anaerobic exercise.

When you're at middle age or later, you have to add anaerobic exercise to your fitness regimen if you want to be fit. It burns more calories and, thus, more fat than aerobic exercise; it strengthens and develops muscle tissue (hello, increased metabolism); and it helps build and retain bone mass. In fact, if you *don't* engage in anaerobic exercise as you get older, you'll lose muscle and bone mass (opening the door to osteoporosis), slow your metabolism, gain fat, and encourage deterioration of your internal organs and your cardiovascular system. We know — tough argument to beat.

If you belong to a gym or health club, you can use strength-training machines to get anaerobic exercise. At home, you can use free weights. Just keep the following tips in mind:

- ✔ **You don't have to invest a lot of time.** Just 30 minutes twice a week — three times, if you want superior fitness — gives you the anaerobic benefits you need.

- ✔ **One set of repetitions should be enough.** Make sure to use a weight that's challenging for the last two or three reps to get the best benefit.

- ✔ **Listen to your body.** If something doesn't feel right, immediately stop what you're doing. The "no pain, no gain" statement is false and can be dangerous.

Often forgotten: Stretching

Don't forget about this one. Stretching increases your range of motion, prevents muscle strain and injuries, helps your joints stay healthy, increases circulation and blood flow, relaxes the body, improves coordination, and allows you to recover more quickly from your workouts. Not enough for you? Stretching also helps you feel mentally alert and reduces anxiety and stress.

Here are some stretching pointers:

- **Stretch to the point of gentle tension.** You shouldn't create pain when you stretch, but you want to stretch the muscles as far as you can *without* creating pain. You want to stretch your muscles in a slow, gradual, and controlled manner through their full range of motion. Hold your stretches for 15 to 30 seconds in the farthest comfortable position.

- **No bouncing!** Bouncing causes trauma to the muscles. When a muscle is damaged, it must heal itself with scar tissue. The scar tissue tightens the muscle, making you feel less flexible. When you feel less flexible, you tend to bounce your muscles in order to stretch. The bouncing causes more trauma to the muscles. Avoid this vicious cycle by not bouncing your muscles to begin with.

- **If your time is limited, hold your stretches for shorter periods of time.** The body is connected like a chain link, so if you stretch many areas for short periods, you reach your major muscle groups.

- **Stretch after you exercise.** You spend all your energy stretching, exercising on a treadmill, and pushing some weights around. Now you're supposed to stretch *again?* Because body temperature is highest after cardiovascular exercise and strength training, stretching at this time enables you to reach your maximum range of motion.

Seeking a Mind-Body Connection

Mind-body fitness asks your mind *and* your muscles to be present and accounted for, and to stay intentionally connected to each other. You pay attention to what you're feeling in your muscles as well as to your breathing. Through this focus comes the contemplative state attributed to mind-body practices, including yoga, tai chi, and Pilates.

Yoga, tai chi, and Pilates not only take inches off your thighs and midsection, but they can reduce everyday stress and give you the confidence you need to operate at a higher level of consciousness.

Yoga

There are various styles of yoga, but hatha yoga puts an emphasis on physical forms to help the mind and, therefore, helps your body and your mind get fit. Hatha yoga (which is typically the style of yoga offered at health clubs and on DVDs) also helps you reduce your stress level, improve your flexibility, increase your strength, and improve your posture (which helps decrease or eliminate lower-back pain).

You can do yoga at home — numerous yoga DVDs are on the market, for a variety of experience and skill levels. Or you can take yoga in a class at your local health club, adult-education center, or community college.

Tai chi

Tai chi is an ancient martial art based on Taoist philosophy, which has adopted many features from Buddhism. Tai chi stresses inward focus and moving slowly through forms that require great balance and control.

To Westerners who traditionally think of exercise as working up a sweat, increasing the heart rate, and maybe even hurting a little, it seems like some kind of a joke that something that looks like adults playing freeze tag could actually be a legitimate exercise. But it really is — you can raise your heart rate, gain strength via deep knee bends and sweeping arm movements, increase your flexibility, and improve your balance. Tai chi is beautiful to watch and peaceful to perform.

Check with your local health club to see if it offers tai chi classes — they aren't as pervasive as yoga classes, but tai chi is on the rise. Or check your phone book for local suggestions.

Pilates

Pilates (pih-*lah*-teez), a series of low-impact flexibility and muscle exercises, was developed by a German fitness guru named Joseph Pilates back in the 1920s. It's a structured method where participants move through exercises either on the floor or on various machines that emphasize mental focus on muscle control and alignment. Core strengthening — of the back and abdominals — is the real gem of this method. (Lower-back pain may be a thing of your past if you take up Pilates.)

Pilates is hugely popular — your health club probably offers a class. You can also do it at home, though you may be better off starting with a class and learning the basics with an instructor.

Chapter 2

The ABCs (and D) of Medicare

In This Chapter

▶ Getting a grip on Medicare and how to qualify

▶ Checking out Medicare's benefits and costs

▶ Figuring out when and how to enroll in Medicare

▶ Discovering how to decrease your costs and increase your benefits

▶ Knowing where to go for more Medicare info

*A*s you near 65, you're likely facing the mysteries of Medicare for the first time — and oh what a mystery it can be. You need to know whether you'll qualify, how to sign up, and how the different parts of the program — each with its own benefits and costs — fit together. This chapter takes the mystery out of Medicare so you know what to expect when you reach that magic milestone of 65.

Knowing When You Qualify

Medicare is the only national healthcare program in the United States, and it's enduringly popular among people who use it. Though Medicare doesn't pay all your medical bills, it still gives a lot of protection against today's high healthcare costs if you don't have other health insurance. And, unlike other forms of health insurance, you can't be excluded from Medicare, or pay more for it, because of advancing age or the state of your health. How's that for your tax dollars at work?

To qualify for Medicare, you must meet certain rules. We break it down in the following sections.

If you're age 65 or older

You qualify for Medicare as soon as you reach age 65 if you *or* your spouse has worked long enough to entitle you to Social Security or Railroad Retirement benefits, even if you're not yet receiving them. You usually need at least 40 credits (amounting to about ten years of work) to become eligible for these retirement benefits, which are paid through monthly checks. Anyone with enough work credits can claim these benefits from the age of 62 onward, though doing so means accepting lower payments than when starting at or after full retirement age. (For people born between 1943 and 1954, full retirement age is now 66.) But remember — even if you claim these benefits early, you still have to wait until age 65 to qualify for Medicare.

The annual statement you receive from Social Security says whether you qualify for Medicare or, if you're not eligible yet, when you will be. If you lose your statement, call Social Security at 800-772-1213 to ask for a replacement.

If you're younger than 65 and have disabilities

You're entitled to Medicare at any age if you have a severe illness, injury, or disability that prevents you from earning more than a certain amount of money each month *and* you've received Social Security disability benefits for at least 24 months. These months need not be consecutive. Anyone diagnosed with Lou Gehrig's disease (amyotrophic lateral sclerosis, or ALS) doesn't have to wait 24 months to join Medicare. If you think you may qualify and want to find out the earnings limits that apply to your circumstances, call Social Security at 800-772-1213 or go to www.ssa.gov.

You're entitled to Medicare at any age if you have end-stage renal disease (ESRD) — usually defined as needing a kidney transplant or regular dialysis — *and* if you or your spouse has paid into Social Security through work for a certain length of time. This period depends on how old you are.

Examining Costs and Coverage in Medicare's Four Parts

Medicare has never been a single unified program in which you pay just one premium to belong and a certain amount for each medical service you use. Instead, Medicare evolved over time and now has four parts, each covering different types of medical care and requiring different payments.

Part A

Part A is insurance that pays most of your costs when you're a patient in a hospital and also, in some circumstances, if you're in a skilled nursing facility or hospice, or are receiving treatment from a home healthcare agency. When you turn 65 and have enough work credits, you instantly qualify for Part A.

If you're eligible for Medicare, you pay no monthly premium charges for Part A. (That's because you, or your spouse, already paid payroll taxes for Medicare in a job.) Services received through Part A, however, aren't free; for example, when you go into the hospital, you pay the first chunk of expenses until you meet the deductible, an amount set by law that usually goes up every year ($1,068 in 2009).

This amount isn't an annual deductible. Instead, it applies to every *benefit period* (the time you're treated in the hospital for a particular spell of illness or injury). If you go into the hospital for a *different* illness or injury, you start a new benefit period and again pay the deductible before coverage kicks in and the payment cycle starts over. There's no limit to the number of benefit periods you can use.

Part A covers the following inpatient services:

- A semiprivate room.
- Regular nursing care.
- All meals provided directly by the hospital or nursing facility.

✔ Other services provided directly by the hospital or nursing facility, including lab tests, prescription drugs, medical appliances, and rehabilitation therapies.

✔ A temporary stay (up to 100 days) in a nursing home or hospital under the skilled-nursing-facility benefit. This benefit is available *only* when nursing or rehabilitation care is necessary following at least three days in the hospital with a related illness or injury.

Part B

Part B is insurance that helps you pay to see a doctor and use services outside of a hospital or nursing facility. Part B is voluntary, meaning you can choose whether you want it and, depending on your circumstances, when to sign up.

If you're 65 or older, you can purchase Part B coverage even if you don't qualify for Part A. To do so, you must be an American citizen or a legal resident who has lived in the United States continuously for five years.

Part B requires you to pay a monthly premium, even if you or your spouse paid taxes for Medicare while working. The Part B premium amount is set annually ($96.40 per month in 2009) and generally goes up from year to year. Most people pay the same premium. However, those with high incomes (more than $85,000 per year in 2009) pay more, and those with very low incomes may receive state help for paying these premiums, if they qualify. Part B also requires you to pay an annual deductible, determined by law ($135 in 2009), which is the out-of-pocket amount you pay for medical care at the beginning of the year before coverage kicks in. You also have to pay a share of the cost of services that Medicare covers — usually 20 percent of the bill.

Part B covers

✔ Approved medical and surgical services from any doctor who accepts Medicare patients, anywhere in the nation

✔ Diagnostic and lab tests done outside hospitals and nursing facilities

✔ A certain number of preventive services and screenings, such as flu shots and mammograms

✔ Some medical equipment (for example, wheelchairs)

✔ Some outpatient hospital treatment received in an emergency room, clinic, or ambulatory surgical unit

✔ Inpatient prescription drugs given in a hospital or doctor's office, usually by injection (such as chemotherapy drugs for cancer)

✔ Some coverage for physical, occupational, and speech therapies

✔ Outpatient mental healthcare (50 percent of approved costs)

✔ Approved home health services not covered by Part A

A wide range of medical services — such as dental, vision, and hearing care (including hearing aids); routine checkups; and outpatient prescription drugs — falls outside Part B's coverage zone.

Part C

The previous two sections outline costs and coverage under *traditional* or *original Medicare,* which earned the name because it follows the basic design of the program originally laid out in 1966.

But Medicare also offers an alternative to the traditional program in the form of a range of health plans that mainly provide managed care. These plans are run by private companies, which decide each year whether to stay in the program. This health-plan program is called Medicare Advantage (or Medicare Part C).

In most cases, you pay a monthly premium for a Medicare Advantage (MA) plan — with the amount varying from plan to plan — on top of the regular Medicare Part B premium. Some plans, however, don't charge an extra premium, and a few also pay all or some of the Part B premium for their members. You pay a share of the costs of hospital and outpatient services. These co-pays vary from plan to plan and are usually different from those required in traditional Medicare.

MA plans must cover all services covered by Part A and Part B in the traditional Medicare program. They may also offer extra services that Medicare doesn't cover — for example, dental and eye care. Most plans include prescription-drug coverage as part of their package.

Unlike traditional Medicare, your choice of doctors and hospitals under most MA plans is likely to be limited to those in the plan's provider network and to the plan's local service area. You also pay more if you go out of network. In a medical emergency, however, the plan must cover the treatment you receive from *any* doctor or hospital.

Part D

Part D is insurance for outpatient prescription drugs — meaning medications you take yourself, instead of having them administered in a hospital or doctor's office. Like Part C, this program is run entirely through many private plans approved by Medicare, each of which has different costs and benefits. You can get Part D through *stand-alone plans* (which cover only prescription drugs and are used mainly by people in traditional Medicare) or through Medicare Advantage health plans that include drug coverage.

Getting with the Program: When and How to Sign Up for Parts A and B

If your 65th birthday is looming and you don't have a clue about how to sign up for Medicare — or even whether you should — you're not alone. In the following sections, we explain when to sign up at the time that's right for you and walk you through the process of enrolling.

It's all in the timing: When to sign up

You can (and should) sign up for at least Medicare Part A around the time you turn 65, whatever your circumstances. It costs nothing to enroll, and you have no premiums to pay. But even if you don't need any Medicare coverage right now, simply getting your name in the system as soon as possible may ensure a smoother ride later on, if and when you decide you want (or need) to sample more of Medicare's offerings.

Exactly when to enroll in Medicare and what services you decide to sign up for depend on your circumstances.

If you already receive Social Security benefits

When we say "Social Security benefits" here, we're referring to Social Security benefits for retirement, dependents, and survivors — or similar benefits for Railroad Retirement. If you're already receiving any of these benefits and haven't yet turned 65, you don't need to sign up for Medicare. In this case, Social Security automatically enrolls you in Medicare Part A and Part B, and you receive your Medicare card in the mail. Coverage starts on your 65th birthday. The same automatic enrollment takes place if you've been getting Social Security disability benefits for two years, regardless of your age.

In both situations, you have the right to cancel Part B coverage if you don't want it (for example, if you already receive medical coverage from an employer or union health plan). But if you're considering canceling because the Part B premium is more than you can afford, you may want to apply for your state's Medicare Savings Program. If you qualify, the state pays your Part B premium, and you automatically become eligible for low-cost prescription-drug coverage under Part D's Extra Help program.

If you don't receive Social Security benefits yet

If you don't receive Social Security benefits by the time you're 65, you need to apply to enroll in Medicare. Timing is very important here — you have a seven-month window, or *initial enrollment period,* to sign up. It begins three months before the month in which you turn 65 and ends three months after your birthday month. So if you're going to celebrate 65 years on June 22, you can sign up any time between March 1 and September 30.

Sooner is better than later. If you enroll early, your coverage starts the month you turn 65. If you wait until after your birthday, it begins on the first day of the month after you enroll.

If you don't sign up for Medicare Part B when you first become eligible, you have to pay a late penalty when you do eventually sign up. (The exception is if you're still working and have group health insurance from an employer or union that's *primary* to Medicare, meaning that your group plan pays your medical bills first.) A late penalty means paying more for Part B in the form of permanently higher premiums — 10 percent higher for every year you could've had Part B but didn't. After your personal deadline for joining Part B has passed, you can sign up *only* during a general enrollment period from January 1 to March 31 each year. Your coverage then begins July 1.

If you have no other health insurance

If you don't currently have health insurance, you'll need Medicare for all your medical coverage. So you'll probably want to sign up for both Part A and Part B. You should sign up for these programs during your seven-month initial enrollment period around the time of your 65th birthday (see the preceding section). If you don't sign up for Part B during this time but decide to do so later, you'll pay a late penalty.

If you work and have group health insurance

If you're still working after the age of 65 and have group health insurance from your employer or union, check with your benefits administrator to find out whether this coverage is primary or secondary to Medicare. *Primary* means your own insurance pays your medical bills first; *secondary* means Medicare pays first and your insurance pays for certain services that Medicare doesn't cover.

So how does this explanation relate to your specific situation? Here are your options:

- ✔ **If your insurance is secondary,** you should sign up for Medicare Part B within your seven-month initial enrollment period (see the earlier section "If you don't receive Social Security benefits yet"). In fact, your employer or union health plan will probably insist on it as a condition for continuing your current coverage. (If your employer has fewer than 20 employees and you're 65 or older, your health plan is automatically secondary to Medicare.)

- ✔ **If your insurance is primary,** you don't need to sign up for Part B at this time. However, when you sign up for

Part A, make sure that Medicare documents that you have primary coverage elsewhere. In the future, if you lose your employer or union coverage, you'll need Medicare to know that you once had it so you can enroll in Part B at that time without incurring a late penalty. If you lose your current coverage, you'll have eight months to sign up for Part B, starting from the end of the month in which you lose coverage. As long as you sign up within this period (or earlier), you won't pay a late penalty, and you'll still have guaranteed access to Medigap insurance (see "Medicare supplementary insurance," later in this chapter).

If you no longer work but have retiree health insurance

After you retire, consider signing up for Part B, even if you still have health insurance from your former employer or union under a retiree plan. Yes, this precaution probably means paying two premiums — and, of course, you have the right not to join Part B if you don't want to (unless your employer or union insists on it as a condition of your retiree coverage). But if at some future date you lose or drop your retiree benefits and need to sign up for Part B at that time, you'll have to pay a late penalty. You won't incur a late penalty if you join Part B within eight months of retiring from your job.

Taking the plunge: How to sign up

When you don't automatically qualify for Medicare — that is, if you're not *already* receiving Social Security or Railroad Retirement payments — you must apply for the program. All you have to do is make one toll-free phone call to the Social Security Administration (*not* Medicare) at 800-772-1213. You can either sign up on the phone or schedule an in-person appointment with your local Social Security office.

Whether on the phone or in person, you can discuss your Medicare needs — such as whether you want to sign up for Part B right now — and whether you want to start receiving Social Security payments as soon as you're eligible. A week or two later, you'll receive your Medicare card in the mail. The card indicates which benefits you've signed up for.

Lowering Costs and Adding Benefits

Medicare has a whole slew of out-of-pocket expenses and doesn't cover all medical services. What, if anything, can you do to lower costs and get more benefits? These sections break down your possible options, depending on various circumstances.

Medicare supplementary insurance

Medicare supplementary insurance is *not* a government program offered by Medicare. It's a separate private insurance you can purchase for an additional monthly premium to fill in some of the gaps in traditional Medicare, which is why it's often called *Medigap*. Depending on the kind of policy you buy, Medigap covers out-of-pocket expenses in Medicare, such as deductibles and co-pays, and may cover extra services (for example, at-home recovery after hospitalization and emergency treatment abroad). Medigap features 12 standard policies, designated A through L, each offering a different range of coverage options — the more options, the more expensive the policy. These policies are sold by many insurance companies at varying premiums. You can compare benefits and costs online at www.medicare.gov or by calling Medicare at 800-633-4227.

 The best time to buy Medigap insurance is within six months of signing up for Medicare Part B (even if you sign up late for Part B), because this timing gives you significant consumer protections.

Medicare Advantage plans (Part C)

Medicare Advantage plans may have lower costs and offer more benefits than traditional Medicare. However, some plans charge higher costs than traditional Medicare for some services and offer only minimal extra benefits. Also, keep in mind that most MA plans limit the choice of doctors and hospitals and may not cover treatment outside of their service areas, except in emergencies.

Veterans benefits

If you qualify for federal health benefits from the Department of Veterans Affairs (VA), you can use them in addition to, or instead of, Medicare. You can also decide which benefits to use for each medical service you need. If you choose the VA for treatment, you must obtain your treatment at a VA facility. Medicare doesn't pay for care at VA facilities but does pay for Medicare-covered medical services that you obtain elsewhere.

If you're a veteran with a low income or a high enough service-related disability rating, you may qualify for free VA care. Whether you're eligible for free care or not, you should consider signing up for Medicare in case you need future services that the VA can't provide or you have to travel too far to get to a VA facility. For more info, call 877-222-8387 or go to www.va.gov/healtheligibility.

Medicaid

Medicaid is a healthcare program for low-income people and is administered by each state, which shares the costs with the federal government. Eligibility depends on the level of your income and savings and varies among the states. If you qualify for both Medicaid and Medicare, you should pay little or nothing for medical treatment — because Medicaid covers Medicare's out-of-pocket expenses — and you have coverage for broader benefits, such as nursing-home care. In addition, you automatically qualify for low-cost prescription-drug coverage under Medicare Part D's Extra Help program.

To find out whether you qualify for Medicaid and how to apply, call your State Health Insurance Assistance Program (SHIP); go to www.medicare.gov/contacts/static/allstatecontacts.asp to find your state's SHIP contact information.

State Medicare savings programs

If you don't qualify for Medicaid, but the Medicare Part B premiums and other costs are still more than you can afford, you may be eligible for help from your state to pay for them. Getting this assistance depends on your income level and any savings you may have. If you qualify, you also automatically receive the full Extra Help benefit under Part D, which provides prescription drug coverage at low cost. Call your State Health Insurance Assistance Program (see the preceding section) to find out whether you qualify for a Medicare savings program and how to apply.

Finding Out More about Medicare

This chapter outlines only the basics of Medicare, just enough to get you on your way. The following resources can give you more detailed info:

- ✔ **Medicare:** Call 800-633-4227 (TTY 877-486-2048) or visit www.medicare.gov for details about Medicare.

- ✔ **Medicare Interactive Counselor:** Go to www.medicare interactive.org for the most comprehensive source of information on Medicare, written especially for consumers in a question-and-answer format.

- ✔ **Social Security Administration:** Call 800-772-1213 (TTY 800-325-0778) or go to www.socialsecurity.gov for information on eligibility and enrollment for Medicare and Social Security retirement benefits.

Medicare-approved HMO, PPO, PDP, and PFFS plans are available to anyone entitled to Part A or enrolled in Part B of Medicare through age or disability. (For Medicare Advantage plans, individuals must have both Part A and Part B.)

Chapter 3

Caring for Your Loved Ones (Including Yourself!)

In This Chapter

▶ Brushing up on parenting skills, for kids of all ages

▶ Finding ways to help your aging loved ones

▶ Taking care of yourself — so you can take care of others

*Y*ou don't need us to tell you that you're part of the sandwich generation — squeezed on all sides and dealing with the needs of all the important people in your life. From your aging parents, to your own kids, and even your grandkids, your loved ones need your time, your energy, and possibly your financial support. When you're spending all your time being there for everyone else, it's easy to overlook your own needs. But the flight attendants have it right: You need to put on your own mask, before you try to help anyone else.

In this chapter, we give you a few strategies for dealing with kids — whether your little ones who haven't left the nest yet, your grown children who've moved back home after college, or your grandchildren. We also offer the straight scoop on what to expect as loved ones age — aging isn't easy, but if you're informed, you'll be better prepared to face the challenges ahead. Finally, we give you concrete tips for avoiding caregiver burnout — you need to take care of yourself in order to help the ones you love.

Parenting Skills for Kids of all Ages

When you were younger, you probably thought that by the time you were in your early 60s, you'd be done with dealing with kids. But somewhere along the line, you realized the inevitable truth: Once a parent, always a parent. Maybe you thought you were done raising kids, only to find that your grandkids have made your home theirs. Perhaps your grown kids moved home after college (or never left after high school), and you're still having to parent them. Or maybe you had kids later in life and your retirement will be more about going to Little League games than hitting the links.

Regardless of your situation, it never hurts to brush up on a few parenting skills that work at any age. In this section, we've got you covered.

Speaking and listening with care

You need an effective way to express your ideas and wants to children of all ages. That's communication. Speak clearly, precisely, and succinctly. If you're too long-winded, your recipient won't hear half of what you're saying.

Be specific about your wants and desires, keeping in mind that they don't always have the same definition that you do. So, when you say, "Please clean your room," be specific about what "clean" means. You may mean "as clean as an operating room before surgery," but they may think that the path from the door to the bed just needs to be a little wider.

Communication also means listening. It's a two-way street: You talk. You listen. Without listening, talking isn't communication.

Being consistent

Being consistent is setting rules and guidelines and not going back on or changing those rules. It means not being wishy-washy. Even when the whining or excuse-making gets to you (and you know it *will*), you need to be firm.

Being consistent is key when dealing with kids of every age. If your kids are adults now, establish the rules of the house. Will they contribute to the household costs? If so, how much? On what day of the month? Are they allowed to smoke or drink in your house? Can they have friends over when you're not home? Can they use your car?

If they start to complain about the rules and say things like, "Hey, I'm an adult — you can't tell me what to do," you can always hand them the classified ads and suggest they look for an apartment of their own, where they can set their own rules.

Following through

Before follow-through can happen, you must give kids a choice. Giving kids choices keeps you from being a bully and enables the kid to have a say in the situation. *Follow-through* means doing what you said you were going to do if your kid doesn't do what you've asked. It means sticking to your original word, an important offshoot of being consistent.

The key here is thinking before you say something because follow-through doesn't always mean bad stuff. Did you really mean it when you said, "Make straight A's and we're going to Europe"? You'd better mean it if you expect to live up to your follow-through.

Making your punishment realistic also helps. For example, don't tell your adult daughter that her rent is due on the first of the month or else you're putting all her clothes out in the yard and changing the locks, unless you're prepared to go that very extreme route. You might instead tell her that if she's late with the rent, you'll cancel the premium cable TV channels that she had to have when she moved back in. And then be sure to follow through.

Remaining patient

Having patience really means planning ahead, understanding the way your kids or grandkids operate, and understanding your own issues and problems enough so that you can recognize that the things they do that bug you are actually your own problems.

Patience means taking more time than is necessary to do something. You may have gotten used to running into the grocery store to pick up a gallon of milk and being back in the car before that story on NPR is over, but if you have your grandkids in tow, everything will take a little longer, and you just have to expect that.

Instead of being so focused on being fast and efficient (skills you may have spent a lifetime perfecting), take a deep breath and enjoy the process. You'll start to see things from a kid's-eye view. (And if that doesn't work, you can always send them back to their parents and do your errands on your own later. That's the joy of grandparenting, right?)

Patience means taking a good look at yourself — asking yourself, "Why does this bug me?" . . . and dealing with the answer.

Managing behavior

Idle hands get into trouble. So do neglected hands. If the children in your life are bored with nothing to do, or if they're craving your attention, they'll find their own means of entertainment and ways to attract your attention.

Behavior management means keeping your kids busy and occupied *most* of the time. Giving them their own free time is a good idea — that way they can use their imaginations to create their own fun. However, if you help organize their time and give them your attention, they won't spend time getting into things they shouldn't. And, while you're at it, praise them when they do something great, like helping you pick up toys or doing something to help around the house. Praise reinforces your kids' perception that what they just did made you happy. Because kids like pleasing their parents, they'll do the things that make you happy again, just to get more praise from you.

So behavior management involves some simple concepts:

✔ **Keeping idle hands busy:** When your grandkids visit for a week, have a plan for how you'll spend much of your time together, and then provide them some age-appropriate activities they can do on their own.

✔ **Giving lots of attention:** Listen to your kids when they want to talk to you. Focus on what they're saying, and show that you're interested. Knock on your son's door and talk to him instead of letting him hole up in his room all dark and brooding.

✔ **Offering praise:** Praise — for people of all ages, not just kids — works wonders. Whether your grandchild colored a picture for you or your adult daughter emptied the dishwasher without being asked, pile on the praise. You can't praise too much.

Recognizing the Challenges of Aging

Hard as it is to believe that you're old enough to have aging people in your life (it doesn't seem that long ago that your dad was yelling at you to turn down the music, your sister was stealing your favorite blouse, or your husband was urging you to check out a cool new jazz band with him), you need to recognize the main signs of aging that you may see in your loved one:

✔ **Slowed reflexes, memory lapses, and "senior moments":** Even in the healthiest people, strength, flexibility, and reaction time diminish with age. The decline actually starts in young adults but isn't noticeable until middle age, when knees aren't what they used to be and pesky memory lapses ("senior moments") appear.

✔ **Diminished senses:** In a normal, healthy, older adult, the five senses (vision, hearing, smell, taste, and touch) tend to decline somewhat with age. A dulling in the perception of pain (the sense of touch) may cause an elderly person to ignore a bedsore, burn, or other injury increasing her risk of serious infection or disability.

✔ **Age-related disease and disability:** Once upon a time, heart attacks, kidney problems, and diabetes were likely to cause an early death. Now they're simply considered "chronic" illnesses — controlled or treated, but not cured. Managing the medications, disabilities, and visits to medical specialists for multiple chronic illnesses can become a time-consuming task.

✔ **Changed family relationships:** A parent who can't take care of herself rattles the foundation of the family. Sometimes loved ones rise to the occasion with calmness and cooperation. More often, long-forgotten childhood rivalries and jealousies raise their ugly heads.

✔ **Diminished interest in activities they once enjoyed:** As your loved one ages, you may notice him withdrawing from the activities he used to love. Many of these changes in interest can be connected to overall health. Lack of feeling good, diminished eyesight or hearing, difficulty walking very far, and other changes related to aging can all impact how your loved one engages with the world. (All the more reason for you to explore Chapter 1 and start taking care of yourself now so that you enter retirement fit and healthy!)

Avoid the mistaken belief that taking care of your frail parent is "parenting your parent." Even though many eldercare tasks are the same as child-care tasks, *emotionally* your parent is still your parent. Trying to parent an adult (for example, by speaking to him like a child) ends up with the parent feeling insulted and angry and the caregiver feeling frustrated and ineffectual.

In the following sections, we help you identify whether your aging loved one needs help and outline your options.

Acknowledging that your loved one needs help

It's sometimes hard to admit — even to yourself — that your aging loved one is failing, especially when he assures you that everything is fine and dandy. But figuring out what's needed and then offering help may prolong his independence and prevent a later crisis.

Taking early action prevents more serious problems. If you observe the following warning signs, a thorough assessment of your loved one's situation is in order:

✔ Extreme clutter, especially in a former neatnik's home; clothes strewn about; items that used to be in drawers and cupboards now crowding countertops and other surfaces

✔ Medication bottles left open; uncertainty about what medications she's taking, and when and why medications are supposed to be taken; unfilled prescriptions

✔ Unpaid bills; penalties for overdue bills; bill-collection notices

✔ Disheveled and dirty clothes; the same outfit worn over and over again; unkempt hair; body odor (which may indicate loss of bowel and bladder control or difficulty bathing); bad breath (which may indicated an inability to brush or floss, gum disease, or infection in the nose, throat, windpipe, or lungs)

✔ Not much food in the house; no nutritious or fresh food in the house; decayed food in the refrigerator

✔ Confusion, sadness, anxiety, or a lack of interest in friends and former pastimes

✔ Bruises on the body (which may be a sign of falls)

It's always best to double-check. Ask neighbors and friends if they've observed similar problems with your loved one and whether they have concerns.

Understanding your options

Caring for an aging loved one involves an ever-changing set of chores — needs almost always grow. As her frailty increases, you'll need to make more decisions about her care. Here are the main options available to you:

✔ **Remaining in her own home:** Like all adults, older people want to be surrounded by their own things and enjoy the freedom and privacy to do as exactly as they please. You may be able to bring care into your loved one's home, so she doesn't have to leave.

✔ **Living with you:** This arrangement has its pros and cons, to be sure. Providing care yourself is less expensive than hiring others to do so, but this scenario can be draining both physically and emotionally for the caregiver. The benefits may very well outweigh the costs, but you need to be realistic about the challenges, your situation, and any positive or negative implications.

✓ **Assisted living:** The premise behind this option is that living in a homelike group setting (with a menu of services available) enhances and extends an older adult's ability to live with dignity. Residents have private or shared rooms and receive only the services that they need or want. Services include meals, housekeeping, laundry, transportation, recreational activities, shopping assistance, and reminders to take medications. Assisted-living facilities do not provide medical care.

✓ **Nursing homes:** Some people go to nursing homes for a short while to recuperate after a hospitalization. For the elderly who become residents, the nursing home will be the last place they live. People don't live in nursing homes because they like the lifestyle — they live there because they need to have skilled nursing care and supervision within reach 24 hours a day.

Tools and resources are available to help you assess your situation, evaluate options, and make decisions about providing care for your loved one:

✓ **Department of Health and Human Services:** Visit `www.eldercare.gov` to find information aimed at helping aging adults live independently and locate eldercare services in their community.

✓ **USA.gov:** Check out `www.usa.gov/Citizen/Topics/Health/caregivers` for access to various tools and information and resources for caregivers.

Coping with Caregiver Burnout

As a member of the sandwich generation, you're providing care for many members of your family — elderly parents who need your help, younger kids who need (grand)parenting, your spouse who needs your everyday support, and maybe even older kids who've returned to the nest for a short (or not-so-short) time. Taking care of so many people — and trying to make time for self-care, too — can take its toll. When nothing seems interesting, and the present and the future seem hopelessly bleak, you may be experiencing symptoms of *caregiver burnout.* Caregiving can be tremendously satisfying, but the unrelenting responsibilities, challenges, and demands of caregiving can also deplete you physically, emotionally, and spiritually over time, turning simple stress into burnout.

Answering the following questions can help you determine whether you're suffering from the effects of caregiver stress:

- ✔ Do you frequently feel blue?
- ✔ Do you feel fatigued despite the amount of rest you get?
- ✔ Do you have trouble falling asleep or staying asleep?
- ✔ Have you lost interest in your work, hobbies, friends, children, or grandchildren?
- ✔ Have you been careless about your own health and medical needs?
- ✔ Are you smoking or drinking more?
- ✔ Has your appetite increased or decreased?
- ✔ Are your emotions reeling out of control?

A single "yes" answer may be a sign of caregiver stress. Two or more affirmative answers are an even greater indication that you may be suffering from stress.

Don't ignore such warning signs. Older caregivers who experience caregiver stress (and have chronic health conditions to boot) have a 63 percent greater chance of dying prematurely than people of a similar age and health who are not experiencing caregiver stress.

Reduce stress and prevent burnout

Try the following strategies to reduce or prevent caregiver stress:

- ✔ **Lighten up.** Seek situations and experiences that make you laugh (like reruns of TV sitcoms) and see the humor in the funny things that life presents to you.

- ✔ **Look for ways to save energy and time.** For example, try shopping by catalog or online. Some grocery stores take phone orders and will have your groceries ready for you to pick up. Shop during off-hours (early is great).

- ✔ **Practice what you preach.** You provide nutritious meals for your family. If you're caring for an elderly parent, you get her up, see that she exercises, and are always on the lookout for things to entertain and relax her. Give yourself the same type of care that you provide others.

✔ **Seek peer support.** No one understands you better than people who are going through a similar experience — they know what it's like to be frustrated when a grown child doesn't seem eager to leave the nest a second time or when daily visits to an elderly parent start putting a strain on other family relationships. (See "Seeking out support," later in this chapter, for more information.)

✔ **Use relaxation techniques.** Simply closing your eyes and visualizing comforting peaceful scenes, listening to music, or meditating may refresh you.

✔ **Discover a new hobby or reestablish an old one.** Scrapbooking, woodworking, watercolor painting, or nature photography are just a few of the creative pastimes that have stress-fighting restorative powers.

✔ **Rotate chores.** Ask family and friends to occasionally (or regularly) relieve you of some of the more mundane but time-consuming tasks.

✔ **Compartmentalize tasks.** Break up big jobs (like preparing Dad's home so that he can live independently after his stroke) into tiny parts (for example, installing grab bars and railings). Then break those parts into smaller components (for example, buying the supplies at the hardware store, arranging a convenient time for installation, deciding where to place the devices). Focus on one small component at a time so as not to be overwhelmed by the big job.

✔ **Seek professional help if the stress seems overwhelming.** A short course of professional counseling can lead to a period of personal growth for you. And don't worry: Lots of people of all ages and backgrounds talk to therapists — there's no shame in seeking help.

✔ **Take advantage of respite care if you're caring for an elderly parent full-time.** Regular breaks help prevent burnout. (See the next section for more on respite care.)

Recognizing the benefits of respite care

If you're the primary caregiver to an aging loved one, you're particularly prone to caregiver burnout, and you may want to take advantage of respite care. *Respite care* is an arrangement in which a substitute caregiver enters the scene to give you a break. For example, a relative or close friend drops by the house for three hours twice a week to keep your loved one company while you do whatever you please. This simple remedy prevents stress, burnout, and downright collapse.

Respite works best when your time off is spent on activities that refuel, relax, or energize you.

Finding respite care referrals takes energy, but it's worth every ounce of effort. The following are places to call for services or referrals:

- ✔ **Local area agencies on aging:** These agencies have different names in different states. You can find your local agency by calling the Eldercare Locator at 800-677-1116.

- ✔ **Your state department of aging:** You can find the number in your telephone directory. Ask whether your state is one of the few that offers funds to pay for respite care. If the answer is "yes," keep your fingers crossed when you ask about a waiting list.

- ✔ **Houses of worship:** Many churches, synagogues, and other religious institutions can refer you to services.

- ✔ **Adult daycare centers:** You can find the numbers of these agencies in telephone directories. A number of daycare programs have special respite programs that include overnight options.

- ✔ **Skilled-nursing facilities:** These facilities are great if you need extended time off, although they can be costly.

- ✔ **Word-of-mouth recommendations:** Ask around. Someone you work with or a friend of a friend may have had a truly dedicated caring person look after her loved one. Call your parent's doctor for a referral.

Introduce the respite worker as a friend. Always tell your parent where you're going and when you'll return. For good measure, write down the information on a reminder note that your parent can read.

Seeking out support

Support works! Decades of research show that that people benefit tremendously from seeking support from their peers.

Other people in your situation can give you a fresh perspective, tried-and-true ideas for solving dilemmas, and information about resources you never knew existed. Other benefits include experiencing less anxiety and less depression, as well as feeling helpful to others in the same boat.

The following suggestions can help you find support groups in your area:

- The **Alzheimer's Association** provides contact information for support groups for caregivers of sufferers of Alzheimer's disease and related disorders. Call 800-272-3900 or go to www.alz.org to find your local Alzheimer's Association chapter.

- The **American Stroke Association** operates the Stroke Family Warmline at 800-553-6321. Telephone counseling for stroke survivors and their caregivers is provided by caregivers themselves. Counselors can refer you to a support group in your area.

- The **Family Caregiver Alliance** provides callers with referrals for support groups in the caller's area. Call 800-445-8106 or go to www.caregiver.org.

- **Hospital social services or social-work departments, YMCA or YWCA branches, and houses of worship** may also have support groups. Check your local Yellow Pages to locate these resources and keep your eyes peeled for announcements of meetings in local newspaper community calendars.

- The **National Self-Help Clearinghouse** can refer callers to support groups in their area. Call 212-817-1822, e-mail info@selfhelpweb.org, or go to www.selfhelp.org for information.

- The **Well Spouse Foundation** is a national group offering support to the wives, husbands, and partners of chronically ill or disabled people. Call 800-838-0879, e-mail info@wellspouse.org, or go to www.wellspouse.org.

Chapter 4

Managing Your Retirement Savings So You Don't Run Out

In This Chapter

▶ Investing your money wisely

▶ Knowing how much you can withdraw and when

▶ Coming up with a budget

▶ Breaking down expenses into needs and wants

▶ Deciding whether to go back to work

*M*any of the major stresses people face as they near retirement are all about money: Will I have enough to retire? How much do I need? How do I make sure my money lasts as long as I do? Given the current economic climate — where your home and stocks may not be worth as much as you anticipated — the stress is not unfounded. In this chapter, we fill you in on the big questions you need to ask yourself, so that you can enjoy your retirement instead of worrying about it.

Investing the Money You Have

By the time you reach retirement, the goal is to have a sizeable nest egg that you can tap as you enjoy your retirement years. Investing your nest egg properly, whatever size you have, is critical to extending its life throughout your life span. In this section, we show you how.

Allocating your investments

Many people think that the most important aspect of managing a portfolio is picking the right stocks, bonds, and mutual funds. They're wrong. The individual stocks, bonds, or mutual funds account for only 5 percent to 10 percent of a portfolio's success. More than 90 percent of that success can be credited to the way you allocate your assets among stocks, bonds, and money-market instruments. Proper asset allocation involves five key factors:

- ✔ **Your investment goal:** Why are you saving? That's probably an easy answer — to have enough money in retirement. But you may be thinking you want to start a business or help your grandchildren go to college.

- ✔ **Your time horizon:** How long will you have until you're going to need the money? When you need the money impacts how you should invest it. (See "Changing your strategies as you age," later in this chapter.)

- ✔ **Your risk tolerance:** If market fluctuations keep you up at night, you have a minimal understanding of investing, or you fear losing more than 25 percent of your assets in a few weeks, you're likely a conservative investor. Keep some stocks in your portfolio to insure that your funds grow throughout your retirement, but consider picking a balanced mutual fund or a life-cycle mutual fund that manages the risk for you without taking any great swings.

    If you're comfortable with the ups and downs of the market, you know the ins and outs of investing, and can accept significant short-term losses in a down market, you're likely an aggressive investor, willing to take more risk with your portfolio to grow your money.

- ✔ **Your financial resources:** How much do you have in your portfolio? How much you have will impact how well you can diversify your portfolio. Basically, it's not wise to put more than 4 percent of your portfolio in any one investment, such as an individual stock or bond. If you don't have enough to diversify properly, use mutual funds that are already well diversified.

- ✔ **Your investment mix:** How well is your portfolio balanced among cash, stocks, and bonds? The way you mix the three key elements will impact the return you can get. A portfolio invested mostly in cash vehicles (money-market funds and certificates of deposit) will have the lowest return, but it's the safest if your primary concern is loss of principal and you're not worried about taxes or inflation eating away your returns. A portfolio invested only in stocks will have the highest return but is the riskiest. By properly allocating those components, you can reduce risk and still grow your money.

Changing your strategies as you age

Your primary goal is to have the cash you need when you need it without having to take a loss on any part of your portfolio. We can't guarantee that you'll never take a loss — everyone makes a mistake in choosing investment opportunities sometimes. But following the general rule of moving money to cash one to two years before needing it minimizes your risk of taking a loss.

The key thing you want to avoid is being forced to sell a stock or bond in a losing position just because you need the cash. Carefully managing your investment mix as you age helps you avoid this type of crisis.

Follow these steps while managing your portfolio in retirement to minimize your risk of taking a loss:

1. **Shift some stocks to bonds.**

   It's best to shift stock holdings to bonds about three to five years before you need the money. As you age, it's good to be sure that your portfolio balance includes bonds for the money you think you'll need in three to five years. That way, you can count on a higher level of growth than cash accounts offer, but your principal is less likely to be at risk.

   You can, of course, convert your stock immediately to cash holdings and not touch your bond holdings if the stock market is up and the bond market is down.

2. **Shift some bonds to a cash vehicle.**

   Convert your bond holdings from Step 1 into cash when you think you're one or two years away from needing the money. Giving yourself that much time will enable you to convert the bonds at a good time, when you'll get the best return on your bonds.

Your time horizon for needing the money is a critical factor in deciding where to put your funds. You don't want to be caught in a down market when you need to sell stocks or bonds. You can avoid being caught by shifting money that you know you'll need in the next two years into a cash vehicle, such as a money-market fund or a certificate of deposit. You won't earn much on the money, but your principal will be safe.

Taking Out Your Money: The Official Rules

Every retirement savings plan has slightly different rules regarding when you may start to draw the money and how much you must withdraw. Some have rules that require you to start withdrawing the money by a particular date, while others leave the decision about when you want to start taking out the money completely in your hands.

When you must start to draw money

When you have to start taking out the money will depend on the type of retirement account you have:

- **401(k)s and 403(b)s:** You can leave your money in the account if you go back to work after retirement, but no matter what you do, when you reach age 70½ you'll have to start taking out your money. You can't delay it longer than that.

- **Profit-sharing plan:** If your company offered a profit-sharing plan, its withdrawal rules will be the same as those for a 401(k). You'll have a 10 percent penalty if you withdraw the funds before age 59½, and you'll have to pay income tax on the funds as you withdraw them.

- **Traditional IRAs:** If you have a traditional IRA, you can't start withdrawing your funds without penalty until the age of 59½. You also must start taking the funds, even if you don't need them, once you reach age 70½.

If you retire early and want to draw the funds sooner or you decide you need the money before age 59½, you'll likely face a penalty of 10 percent when withdrawing the funds. You'll also have to pay taxes due on the amount of money you withdraw. You can avoid the penalty but not the income taxes if you take the money out for higher education, first-time home purchase, or death or disability.

Whenever you take funds out of a traditional IRA, you'll have to pay income taxes on the money withdrawn. The one exception to this rule is that, if you put money into a non-tax-deductible traditional IRA, your contributions to the fund are not taxable because you paid taxes on them before depositing the money in the IRA, but you do pay taxes on any gains made with the money contributed.

Be sure you keep your non-taxable traditional IRA separate from all other IRAs. If you co-mingle the funds of a tax-deductible IRA and a non-tax-deductible IRA, you'll need to pay income taxes on all the money.

✔ **SIMPLE or SEP-IRAs:** If your employer sponsored a SIMPLE or SEP-IRA for you, the rules for withdrawal are the same as they are for a traditional IRA. You own the account from the day your company opens it for you, and you'll be able to withdraw the money the same way you would with a traditional IRA. If you keep the money in your SIMPLE IRA for less than two years, you'll have to pay a 25 percent penalty rather than just a 10 percent penalty.

✔ **Roth IRA:** The Roth IRA is the only type of retirement savings you have that is not taxed as you withdraw the money as long as you wait until age 59½. If you need to withdraw the money before that age, you can withdraw your annual contributions tax-free.

If you need to withdraw the money for the purpose of buying a house for the first time, you can withdraw the money from your Roth IRA tax-free, provided the money was deposited in the Roth IRA for at least five years. If you withdraw the money for any other purpose, you'll need to pay taxes on the earnings, but not on your initial contributions.

How much you must withdraw

When you reach the age of 70½, you don't have a choice: Even if you're working, you have to start withdrawing funds from your retirement savings accounts. The only exception to this are funds in your Roth IRA — there are no mandatory withdrawal rules for the Roth IRA.

The amount you must withdraw will be lower than the amount you'll likely withdraw after you start depending on your retirement savings to meet your budget. But you probably won't have to worry about these rules unless you're working and not ready to start funding your retirement with your savings. Many working retirees decide to leave the money in their retirement savings accounts as long as possible, and some even add to them.

If you don't take out the minimum amount required, you'll have to pay a 50 percent penalty on any shortfall. It's a hefty penalty, so don't make this mistake.

The IRS developed two tables to help you determine how much you have to withdraw each year. One table assumes your beneficiary is *not* more than ten years younger than you; the other assumes your beneficiary *is* more than ten years younger than you. You can find these tables in IRS Publication 590 online at `www.irs.gov/publications/p590/ar02.html` (scroll down to Appendix C in this publication).

The IRS tables provide you with a distribution factor to use in determining how much you can withdraw. To calculate the amount you must withdraw each year after you reach 70½, divide the amount you have in your IRA account by the distribution factor. For example, if you're 72 years old and your spouse is 62 years old, your distribution factor is 25.6. Let's say you have $300,000 in retirement funds. Divide $300,000 by 25.6, and the amount that you must withdraw at age 72 to avoid a 50 percent penalty is $11,718.75.

Even the most conservative financial planner will tell you that it's safe to withdraw 4 percent yearly from your retirement savings. A 4 percent withdrawal would total $12,000. So you can see the minimum withdrawals are slightly below that and shouldn't create a major burden for you even if you're working and have to pay income taxes on your salary, Social Security, and the distribution.

If you don't need the mandatory distribution funds because you're still working, you can always deposit them in a Roth IRA. (There is no age limit for depositing money in a Roth.) That way your money can grow tax free for the rest of your life.

If you never need it, you can leave it to your heirs. ***Remember:*** You're never obligated to withdraw funds from a Roth IRA.

Making Sure Your Savings Lasts as Long as You Do

The rule of thumb most financial advisors give their clients is that they can safely withdraw 4 percent of their retirement savings each year and their money will last for their lifetime.

That's a short and quick rule that does work, but if you need more income than that from your portfolio, you may want to take a bit more risk with how you allocate your asset mix. By holding a greater percentage of stocks — which are riskier than bonds or mutual funds but which often deliver a higher return — you may be able to withdraw more annually.

Table 4-1 looks at various asset mixes between stocks and bonds. It then shows you what percentage you can withdraw based on your risk tolerance and the number of years you expect to live in retirement.

We group withdrawal rates into three risk levels based on your chances of having enough money throughout your retirement years. We also developed withdrawal rates based on the number of years you expect to live in retirement.

In looking at the chart, notice that there really isn't much advantage to picking an asset mix for your portfolio riskier than 50 percent stocks and 50 percent bonds.

We developed Table 4-1 using data from a study of historical stock returns over a 70-year period. Stocks historically averaged a return between 10 percent and 12 percent, bonds historically averaged a 4 percent to 6 percent return, and cash historically averaged 3 percent. We used a 3 percent inflation rate average for this chart. The withdrawal rates we show you in Table 4-1 are adjusted for inflation.

If you expect to live more than 30 years in retirement, you probably should choose the safe route and not increase your withdrawal rate above 4 percent. You may want to play it safe with 3 percent.

Table 4-1	How Much You Can Withdraw Annually					
Asset Mix	Chance Your Assets Will Last throughout Your Lifetime	15 Years	20 Years	25 Years	30 Years	
100% stocks	90%–100%	6%	4%	4%	4%	
	75%–90%	7%	6%	5%	5%	
	<50%	11%	8%	7%	7%	
75% stocks, 25% bonds	90%–100%	6%	5%	4%	4%	
	75%–90%	7%	6%	5%	5%	
	<50%	10%	9%	8%	7%	
50% stocks, 50% bonds	90%–100%	6%	5%	4%	4%	
	75%–90%	7%	6%	5%	5%	
	<50%	10%	8%	7%	7%	
25% stocks, 75% bonds	90%–100%	5%	4%	4%	3%	
	75%–90%	6%	5%	4%	3%	
	<50%	9%	6%	5%	5%	
100% bonds	90%–100%	5%	4%	3%	<3%	
	75%–90%	6%	4%	3%	3%	
	<50%	7%	5%	4%	4%	

If you do want to keep growth in your portfolio, be sure to convert some of your portfolio to cash at least two years before you'll need it to be sure you're not stuck selling stocks or bonds during a downturn in the market. You should also be sure to sell stocks and use the money to invest in bonds when you're about five years away from needing it.

If you've never managed a portfolio before, don't try to do this totally on your own at first. Work with a financial planner to put together your strategy for withdrawing your funds. Even if you do have a lot of portfolio experience, it doesn't hurt to pay for a few hours of consultation time with a financial planner to be sure your assumptions are correct. A third-party view from someone who isn't as personally involved in the outcome is always a good idea when you're making significant financial choices that will impact your ability to maintain your desired lifestyle in the future.

Use the resources of the Financial Planning Association to find a good advisor near your home. Go to `www.fpanet.org/public`.

Determining Your Budget

You won't need the same amount of money throughout retirement. In fact, most people move through at least three phases of life during retirement. You also need to budget for different types of things than you did while you were working. In this section, we review budgeting for the phases of retirement and what items you need to include in your budget.

Budgeting for each phase of retirement

When you're budgeting for retirement, you have to think of retirement in three phases:

> ✔ **Active phase:** During this phase of your life, you'll still be very active, whether you completely retire or go back to work. You want to take time to enjoy the money you socked away while working before retirement. You also may decide to go back to work to supplement what you saved. You'll need extra money for travel and other

things you dreamed of doing during retirement. Your living costs may be a bit less than they were when you were working, but not much.

✔ **Passive phase:** During this phase of your life, you start to slow down. You're probably well enough to continue living on your own, but probably not well enough to continue traveling or doing the other activities you did during the active phase. Your living costs will actually be the cheapest during this phase, because you'll likely cut back on travel, entertainment, transportation costs, and clothing purchases.

✔ **Dependent phase:** Some people avoid this phase — they're the lucky few. Odds are, you'll get to a phase in your life where you must be dependent on others for help to meet your daily needs, such as help with bathing, dressing, and preparing food. Your living costs could actually be the highest in this phase of life, especially if you need to enter an assisted-living facility or nursing home. Either way, your medical costs will likely be much higher than in the active and passive phases of retirement.

You actually need to develop three estimated budgets to calculate what you might need in retirement. You can't be sure exactly how long you'll live in retirement, but by considering your family history and your current health, you can make an educated guess.

 MSN Money has an excellent life-expectancy calculator at `http://moneycentral.msn.com/investor/calcs/n_expect/main.asp`.

Accounting for everything

For budget purposes, you'll probably have most of the same line items on your budget as you did while you were working full-time, but you'll drop some costs (for example, commuting, business gifts, and professional dues) and add others (such as increased health-insurance premiums, increased healthcare expenses, and increased travel and leisure costs).

In the following sections, we break down expenses into needs and wants. Focus on your needs first, and then add in as many of your wants as you can afford.

Needs: Things you can't live without

The following items are the most essential parts of any budget:

- **Healthcare:** Your healthcare costs will likely take a much larger chunk out of your budget than they did when you were younger. Before you qualify for Medicare, you'll likely be paying all your medical insurance and expenses out of pocket. Even after you do qualify for Medicare, you need to pay premiums for Medicare Part B and Part D. You'll also have out-of-pocket costs for deductibles and co-pays, and you'll likely have additional coverage to pay for things Medicare doesn't cover. (See Chapter 2 for more on Medicare.)

- **Food and shelter:** Your shelter costs may change depending on whether you stay in your current home, move to a smaller home, or keep two homes (for example, one where you live now, and one in a warmer climate for the winter months). Your food costs will depend on whether you want to eat out more or save money and do more cooking at home.

- **Taxes:** Even in retirement, you have to budget for taxes, particularly those related to you retirement pension and/or savings. You won't have to pay taxes to Social Security and Medicare unless you go back to work, and then you'll only have to pay taxes on the money you earn working.

  Most states reduce property taxes and some reduce state income taxes when you reach retirement age, so be sure to check out tax rules in your state after you retire. The Retirement Living Information Center maintains a state-by-state breakdown on taxes at `www.retirement living.com/RLtaxes.html`.

- **Savings and investments:** Most people don't add to their savings and investments during retirement. But if you do plan to work, you may be able to budget for additional savings and investments.

- **Insurance:** You probably won't see a big difference in most of your insurance costs. Your health insurance may increase, though, in retirement.

- **Debt:** By the time you reach retirement, the goal is to be rid of most of your debt. On a fixed income, debt becomes more of a burden as the basics of life continue to rise, but your income doesn't. But if you do still have debts to pay, add them to your budget figures.

Wants: Things you can live without

The following are wants — things that you probably can't imagine your life without but that you could give up if you absolutely had to. Include room in your budget for as many of these as you can afford after your needs are met:

- ✔ **Entertainment:** Entertainment costs will likely go up during the active phase, but they'll likely drop some during the passive phase. If you have a big family, you may need to budget for more family gatherings at your house and the additional costs for food and other expenses to host those gatherings. In the dependent phase, you probably won't need to plan for entertainment.

- ✔ **Leisure and travel:** Leisure and travel costs will vary greatly in the three phases of retirement. Initially, they'll probably be higher than they are now, but as you age they'll probably drop. If you're looking forward to a travel-filled retirement, this chapter can help you save for it. (Check out Chapter 5 for ideas on places to go!)

- ✔ **Hobbies:** If you enjoy a hobby, this can take a much bigger chunk of your budget in retirement because you'll have much more time to spend on your hobby (hooray!). Try to guesstimate your increased hobby budget; you may even need to hold yourself back if you don't have enough money for all you want to do.

- ✔ **Pets and plants:** Many people get additional pets during retirement. In fact, studies have shown that aging adults are happier and healthier if they have pets. Plants can also make a room feel more alive. Plan for these increased costs in your budget, unless you know for sure you won't want them.

- ✔ **Philanthropy:** You'll probably cut back on your donations in retirement because you no longer have the extra cash. If you do still plan to keep up a certain level of donations, calculate that in your budget as well.

And keep in mind that you can give back to your community in all kinds of ways that require absolutely no money at all. Volunteer at your local library and read to children. Build houses with Habitat for Humanity (www.habitat. org). Serve meals at your local soup kitchen or drive for Meals on Wheels (www.mealsonwheels.org), getting food to those who need it. These cost-free endeavors require no line in your budget and give you a huge return on your philanthropic investment!

✔ **Professional services:** Finding a financial partner you can trust is key as you enter retirement. You'll want to work with this person, at least in the beginning of your retirement years, to be sure your financial assumptions are correct and you've come up with a good plan for spending down your assets. You should also review your will with an attorney, and be sure that everything is in order for your estate. Expenses for professional services will vary depending on how much you've saved.

Calculating Whether Your Income Is Enough

This is the big question, the one you've been waiting for: Will I have enough to retire? Here's how to calculate the answer:

1. **Calculate your annual budget needs (see "Determining Your Budget," earlier in this chapter).**

2. **Calculate your annual income by adding any annual annuity payouts, pension payouts, Social Security benefits (if you're old enough to collect), retirement savings withdrawals, and any other money you expect to have each year.**

3. **Subtract your budget from your income.**

   The answer will tell you whether you have a surplus or a shortfall. If the number is positive, you have enough money for retirement. If the number is negative, you'll need to find some more money — most likely by working.

If you have a shortfall, you're better off correcting the shortfall by taking a job as soon as possible after retirement. As you get older, working will be increasingly difficult. By bringing in extra income, you may be able to reduce the amount you take out of your retirement savings each year and let your portfolio grow a bit more. And a larger portfolio means you'll be able to increase your income in your later years because you'll be able to withdraw more from your portfolio.

When you do decide to quit work entirely, you can then recalculate your annual payouts by considering the number of years left at that time in retirement. Recalculate your withdrawal rate based on your asset mix and number of years in retirement when you quit.

Making That Critical Decision: Stay Retired or Go Back to Work?

After you get home from your final retirement party and you face a life without having to go into work every day, the initial sense of relief is wonderful — and it may last for years to come. But for many people, staying completely retired is unthinkable — either because they want to work or because they need to. Here are some scenarios of why people need to go back to work:

- ✔ Although Medicare prescription drug coverage helps to some extent, the infamous Medicare Part D *donut hole,* where all of a sudden seniors find they have no coverage for a while, creates financial crises for many people who are dependent on a fixed income and can't afford monthly financial surprises.

- ✔ You may have planned to use the equity in your home for your retirement; now your home isn't what it was worth a few years ago, so you don't have as much as you need.

- ✔ You may just have to admit you didn't save enough to keep up the lifestyle you've become accustomed to and want to continue to enjoy.

Money is not the only reason that people choose to go back to work. Some people just plain miss the professional camaraderie they enjoyed in the workplace and want to return there to reconnect with their professional network.

Other retirees decide they want to go back to school or teach to get the intellectual juices going. Retirement doesn't have to be about golfing, swimming, card playing, and the yearly vacation. You can go back to work, volunteer, or go back to school and still be among the ranks of today's retirees.

Chapter 5

Finally, I Can Relax! Planning to Travel

● ●

In This Chapter

▶ Planning a destination vacation

▶ Hitting the road to see America

▶ Enjoying a "volunteer" vacation

▶ Staying safe, saving money, and leaving the stress at home

● ●

*O*ne of the best parts of getting older is having more time to give you all kinds of options. Here, we've pulled together three amazing destinations — Alaska, Australia, and Cancún and the Yucatán. Plus, we give you the lowdown on hitting the road to see America — who does it, how, and where to go. If you want to use your vacation to give back to people in need, a volunteer vacation will be right up your alley — in this chapter, we give you ideas of places to start. Finally, if traveling makes you a wee bit nervous, never fear: We give you tips to follow to ensure your vacation is a memorable one — for all the right reasons.

Indulging in Adventure: Alaska

What better way to retire than with a true adventure? And what better place for that than Alaska? In this section, we whet your appetite for all things Alaska, filling you in on some of the best Alaska has to offer for that ageless adventurer inside you — the one who can't wait to retire so you can get out and *live!*

The best one-of-a-kind lodgings

When some people travel, they want to feel as though they've really *gone* somewhere. If that sounds like you, you'll appreciate these authentic places for visitors, all of which are brimming with local character:

- **Alyeska Prince Hotel,** 100 Arlberg Ave., Girdwood (☎ **800-880-3880** or 907-754-1111; www.alyeska resort.com): Alaska's grandest luxury hotel, an hour from Anchorage, has a one of a kind location, in an unspoiled mountain valley among huge spruce trees. Skiers can go right from the door to Alaska's best slopes; in the summer, the aerial tram is an easy way for anyone to experience the crisp air and magnificent views.

- **Land's End Resort,** 4786 Homer Spit Rd., Homer (☎ **800-478-0400** or 907-235-0400): The hotel is charming, but the location is what makes it unique. It sits at the very end of a 5-mile-long point of land into Kachemak Bay, one of Alaska's most beautiful bodies of water. You can walk from your room to fish for salmon, or sit back and watch sea otters swim by.

- **Aurora Express Bed and Breakfast,** 1540 Chena Ridge Rd., Fairbanks (☎ **800-221-0073** or 907-474-0949; www. fairbanksalaskabedandbreakfast.com): A family hauled a collection of railroad cars — plus a locomotive and caboose — up a mountain south of Fairbanks and remodeled the interior into a collection of accommodations, some too cute for words, others heavily nostalgic for those who remember the golden age of rail.

The best uniquely Alaskan experiences

Alaska is an adventure because it's unlike anyplace you've ever been. Here are some ways to *know* you're in Alaska:

- **Getting out on the big ice:** More than 36 major glaciers around Juneau flow from a single ocean of ice behind the mountains, the 1,500-square-mile **Juneau Ice Field.** Helicopters from Juneau fly over the immense ice field that lies beyond the mountains bordering the town. Visitors can just look, or join guided hikes on the ice, or even get in a dog sled and go mushing on the glaciers. Contact **Era Helicopters** (☎ **800-843-1947;** www.era aviation.com) for copter tours and dogsled rides.

✔ **Cruising Alaskan waters:** Less than two hours from Anchorage, the port town of Whittier provides access to northwestern Prince William Sound, a world to itself — largely free of people, with 3,500 miles of shoreline enfolded within its islands and deeply penetrating fjords and passages. Glaciers loom on the mountains at the northwestern part of the sound, and on the way to see them, it's commonplace to encounter humpback and orca whales, dolphins, seals, otters, and a variety of birds. Day cruises from Whittier, easy to do as a day trip from Anchorage, compete on price, food service onboard, and number of glaciers you see in a few hours (up to two dozen!). Start with **Major Marine Tours** (☎ **800-764-7300;** www.majormarine.com) and **Phillips Cruises and Tours** (☎ **800-544-0529;** www.26glaciers. com). Expect to spend about $190 per person (between the train fare from Anchorage and the boat fare itself) for this full-day outing.

✔ **Encountering indigenous culture:** The cultural heritage and ways of life of Alaska's indigenous people remain largely intact in many areas of the state, and Alaskan Natives are often interested in sharing their traditions with visitors. At the **Iñupiat Heritage Center,** at Ahkovak and C streets in Barrow (☎ **907-852-5494**), Eskimo culture is alive and well, and in Barrow you can often see subsistence hunters preparing or returning from hunts for whale, caribou, or polar bear. At the town's fascinating cultural center and living museum, you can also see exhibits and dance performances and meet craftsmen selling authentic Iñupiat artwork.

✔ **Visiting a gold-rush town:** The Klondike Gold Rush of 1898, when the non-Native population arrived all at once in search of riches, is the biggest event in Alaska's short history. Nome's gold-rush stories top all. Although most of the historic structures are gone, the town retains a free-wheeling frontier spirit, making it feel more like a gold-rush boomtown than other more tourist-oriented places. Small-time prospectors are still at work here, too. For more information, contact the **Nome Convention and Visitors Bureau,** Front and Division streets (☎ **907-443-6624;** www.nomealaska.org/vc).

Australia: Enjoying the Trip of a Lifetime

There's no better time than retirement to do the things you've always *wanted* to do but never had time for. Enter Australia. Here, we give you a taste of this incredible continent.

The best places to lay your head at night

The big cities offer the high-end chains as well as boutique hotels, but if a trip of a lifetime is what you're after, you can't go wrong with **Hayman** (☎ 800-745-8883 from the U.S. and Canada; www.hayman.com.au) on the Whitsunday Islands in Queensland. It's the most luxurious and glamorous resort in Australia. Check-in is done over a glass of bubbly aboard the resort's sleek launch as you travel from Hamilton Island Airport. You soon find your way through the open-air sandstone lanais, cascading ponds, and tropical foliage to the fabulous hexagonal complex of swimming pools by the sea. Dress is beachwear by day, smart casual at night. Every room, suite, villa, and penthouse has a balcony or terrace, bathrobes, and valet service (and butler service in the penthouses).

Still, with a decent exchange rate and a good supply of moderately priced places to stay, you can find both comfort and bargains throughout Australia, including the following:

- ✔ **North Adelaide Heritage Group,** Adelaide (☎ 08-8272-1355; www.adelaideheritage.com): It's worth coming to Adelaide just for the experience of staying in one of these out-of-this-world apartments, cottages, or suites.

- ✔ **Underground Motel,** Smiths Hill, White Cliffs (☎ 08-8091-6677 outside of Australia): Making the trip out to White Cliffs is worth the effort, just to stay here for the night. All but two of the rooms are underground; they're reached by a maze of spacious tunnels dug out of the rock and sealed with epoxy resin.

- ✔ **Freycinet Lodge,** Freycinet National Park, Tasmania (☎ 03-6225-7000; www.puretasmania.com): We can't praise this eco-friendly lodge enough. Comfortable one- and two-room cabins spread unobtrusively through the bush, connected by raised walking tracks.

The best memory-making experiences

The trip of a lifetime is all about making memories that'll last. Here are some experiences you'll never forget:

- ✔ **Having an Outback adventure:** You'll taste bush food, throw boomerangs, and learn about Aboriginal family values during a half-day tour of the Aborigine-owned **Aboriginal Art & Culture Centre,** 86 Todd St., Alice Springs (☎ 08-8952-3408). **Anangu Tours** (☎ 08-8950-3030; www.anagutours.com) runs a series of walks around and near Uluru (Ayers Rock), in the heart of the Outback. The Anangu are the traditional owners of Uluru. Join them for walks around the Rock as you learn about the "snake men" who fought battles here, pick bush food off trees, throw spears, visit rock paintings, and watch the sun set.

- ✔ **Communing with nature:** The 74 islands of the Whitsundays are best seen from the deck of your own private yacht. Bareboat sailing (or skipper-yourself) is one of the most popular pastimes here, and it's easy to see why as you snorkel over dazzling reefs, fish for coral trout, and feel the wind in your sails. It's on the same latitude as Tahiti, and on the same level of beauty. **Tourism Whitsunday** (www.tourismwhitsunday.com) can furnish you with a complete list of operators.

- ✔ **Hitting the beach:** Azure water, islands dotting the horizon, and white sand edged by vine forests make Mission Beach a real winner. The bonus is that hardly anyone comes here. Cassowaries (giant emulike birds) hide in the rain forest, and the tiny town of Mission Beach makes itself invisible behind the leaves. Contact the **Mission Beach Visitor Information Centre** (☎ 07-4068-7099; www.missionbeachtourism.com) for info.

- ✔ **Seeing animals:** You'll see more native animals on South Australia's **Kangaroo Island** — including koalas, wallabies, birds, echidnas, reptiles, seals, and sea lions — than anywhere else in the country, apart from a wildlife park. And the distances between major points of interest are not great, so you won't spend half the day just getting from place to place. Contact **Tourism Kangaroo Island** (☎ **08-8553-1185;** www.tourkangarooisland. com.au) for accommodations and tour information.

Fun for All Generations: The Yucatán

You've spent your whole life working — you deserve to kick back and relax. Mexico's Yucatán peninsula — home to Cancún and Cozumel, not to mention a rich history (complete with Maya pyramids) — is the perfect place to escape. Whether you want to relax alone on the beach with a book, have a romantic getaway with your spouse or partner, or get your entire family in on the action, the Yucatán has what you're looking for. Plus, you don't have to cash out your 401(k) to do it — compared to other similar destinations, the Yucatán is reasonably priced.

Children are considered the national treasure of Mexico, and Mexicans warmly welcome and cater to children — good news if you're bringing the family with you on your retreat. One of the best destinations for children in Mexico is Cancún. Hotels can often arrange for a baby sitter. Some hotels in the moderate-to-luxury range have playgrounds and pools for children, as well as caretakers who offer activity programs during the day, but few budget hotels offer these amenities. All-inclusive resorts make great options for family travel.

The best places to stay

If money is no object, Cancún and the southern coast of the Yucatán have no shortage of places to park yourself in style. Perhaps it goes without saying that the **Ritz-Carlton Cancún,** Retorno del Rey 36, off Blvd. Kukulkán, km 13.5 (☎ **800-241-3333;** www.ritzcarlton.com), is one of the finest hotels in Cancún, but what you may not know is that it's considered one of the finest hotels in *Mexico,* and it's the only beachfront hotel in the *world* to be awarded three AAA Five-Diamond ratings.

With its Ritz Kids program (full of supervised activities for children), the Ritz-Carlton makes for a great family destination. Baby-sitting services are also available.

Being on a budget in the Yucatán doesn't mean you have to sacrifice style. There are plenty of well-priced options, and here are two of our favorites:

- ✔ **El Rey del Caribe Hotel, Av. Uxmal,** corner with Nadar, Sm. 2-Am, Ciudad Cancún (☎ **988-884-2028;** www.rey caribe.com): Not only will you find exceptional value here, but you'll also support a true ecological hotel, which uses environmentally sensitive practices from collecting rainwater to composting. Sunny rooms are surrounded by lush jungle landscaping — and all in the heart of downtown Cancún!

- ✔ **Hotel Ojo de Agua,** Supermanzana 2, lote 16, Puerto Morelos (☎ **998-871-0027** or 998-871-0507): For little money you can have a room on the water and access to all manner of non-motorized watersports equipment, including snorkeling and windsurfing. This family-run hotel in Puerto Morelos has friendly and helpful staff, and offers the convenience of its own dive shop and windsurfing rental.

The best things to do

With the ocean as tempting as it is off the Yucatán coast, you're certain to find multiple ways to enjoy it above and below the surface. On dry land, you can also find plenty of ways to fill your days. Here are our favorite things to do:

- ✔ **Snorkeling:** Even if you're not usually the sporting type, you don't want to miss the chance to try snorkeling the local reef system, which is highly acclaimed by divers. The waters offshore are so clear that snorkelers are guaranteed to see clouds of tropical fish in every color of the rainbow, and possibly even a turtle or two. You can see a stunningly beautiful underwater world. One of the best places is El Garrafon Park in Isla Mujeres.

- ✔ **Swimming with dolphins:** In Cancún, the **Parque Nizuc** (☎ **998-881-3030;** www.atlantidacancun.com) aquatic park, home of Wet 'n Wild Cancún, offers guests a chance to swim with dolphins and view these wonderful creatures in their own aquarium, Atlántida. It's a fun place for a family to spend the day, with its numerous pools, water slides, and rides.

- ✔ **Eating where the locals do:** To steep yourself in Yucatecan cuisine and music, head directly to **Labná,** Margaritas 29, next to City Hall and La Habicula restaurant, Santa María (☎ 998-884-3158; www.labna.com), a showcase of Maya moods and regional foods. Thursdays through Saturdays, follow your meal with a live musical performance by popular Maya artists.

- ✔ **Fly-fishing off the Punta Allen and Majahual Peninsulas:** Serious anglers enjoy the challenge of fly-fishing the saltwater flats and lagoons on the protected sides of these peninsulas.

- ✔ **Birding:** The Yucatán is an ornithological paradise, with hundreds of species awaiting the birder's gaze and list. A special place is Isla Contoy, with more than 70 species of birds as well as a host of marine and animal life.

In addition to beautiful beaches, the Yucatán also offers a spectacular glance into this region's rich history through its various architectural sites and ruins. One of our top picks for a day trip in the Yucatán is **Chichén Itzá** (chee-*chin* eat-*zah*). Stand beside the giant serpent head at the foot of the El Castillo pyramid and marvel at the architects and astronomers who positioned the building so precisely that shadow and sunlight form a serpent's body slithering from peak to the earth at each equinox (March 21 and September 21).

Plan Your Own Destination Vacation

You can plan your own trip anywhere in the world by asking yourself what sorts of sights you'd like to see, which country or state you'd like to visit, or what type of activity you'd like to enjoy. Head to www.dummies.com and www.frommers.com for inspiration, ask friends for recommendations, read magazines like *National Geographic Traveler* or *Travel + Leisure* . . . let your mind go wild! Nothing is off limits in this early brainstorming stage!

When you've made your dream-vacation list, head to sites like Travelocity (www.travelocity.com) and TripAdvisor (www.tripadvisor.com) to make your dream a reality.

There, you can book flights, accommodations, car rentals, and even excursions.

On the Road Again: Seeing the USA

Freedom! If you want to sum up road trips in one word, that's it. You're freed from fighting the battle of airports, from having to pay an extra fee for every bag you bring with you, and from sticking to an itinerary you set months ago — if you discover a destination you love, you can stay longer without paying to change a plane ticket. In your car or RV, you're the boss. You go where you want to go, when you want to go, and at whatever pace you please. That's *freedom!*

Discovering something for everyone

Road-tripping isn't just for people who like to sit around campfires with strangers, swapping yarns. It's for everyone:

- ✔ **People with kids:** Road trips are family friendly in the extreme. They're a cheap and convenient way of taking the whole family on vacation. But the simple truth is, kids love road-tripping, and road trips are a great way to temporarily set aside everyone's busy schedules to enjoy some quality family time!

- ✔ **Hikers and bikers:** You can head for state or national parks with great walking and bicycle trails. And after a day of breaking a sweat, you can return to your hotel or the comfort of your own RV and head out the next day for an all-new adventure.

- ✔ **Scenic-highway cruisers:** Do you want to settle into the driver's seat and just cruise? Road-tripping is for you. America's scenic highways were built for slow, easy driving and frequent stops to admire the view or set out a picnic.

- ✔ **Foodies:** There's no better way to take in all the delicious tastes of America than on a road trip. You can sample everything from fresh-from-the-sea Maine lobster with melted butter, to Texas barbecued brisket smoky from the grill, to Santa Maria barbecue along California's coast!

✔ **Music lovers:** When you travel by car or RV, you can tap your toes to the rich sounds of America. From authentic mountain music in the Ozarks to the birthplace of Elvis Presley to rock in all its forms at Cleveland's Rock and Roll Hall of Fame and Museum, a road trip can take you there.

✔ **Sports fans:** Whether you want to head to Cooperstown or see how many baseball parks you can visit in one summer, you can do it on a road trip.

Fun attractions across the U.S.

The world of road-tripping is almost limitless, but if you're looking for some places to start, look no further than this list:

✔ What place says "road trip" louder than **Grand Canyon National Park?** A good way to visit is to take the **Grand Canyon Railway,** 233 N. Grand Canyon Blvd., Williams, Arizona (just off I-40; ☎ **800-843-8724;** www.thetrain. com), a steam train that leaves daily at 10 a.m. year-round from the restored 1908 train station. Passengers ride the refurbished 1928 rail cars the 65 miles north to the canyon, have a few hours for sightseeing, and then return in the late afternoon. Taking the train is a good idea, because Grand Canyon National Park now prohibits private vehicles from the entire South Rim.

✔ The **National Baseball Hall of Fame,** 25 Main St., Cooperstown, New York (☎ **888-42505633** or 607-547-7200; www.baseballhalloffame.org), is one of America's favorite family summer destinations. The legendary "Doubleday baseball" on display is believed to have been the ball used in 1839 when Abner Doubleday invented baseball in Elihu Phinney's cow pasture one afternoon — if, in fact, that ever happened, which some experts doubt. Additional artifacts also are on hand, from Jackie Robinson's warm-up jacket to Joe DiMaggio's locker; Ty Cobb's sliding pads to Yogi Berra's glove; and bats used for record-breaking home runs by Babe Ruth, Roger Maris, Mickey Mantle, Hank Aaron, and Mark McGwire.

✔ The **Rock and Roll Hall of Fame and Museum,** off I-90 in Cleveland, Ohio (☎ **888-764-7625;** www.rockhall.com), designed by I. M. Pei with a glass pyramid reminiscent of the same architect's entrance to the Louvre in Paris, is a great place to spend a day. On life-size mannequins are Leadbelly's 12-string guitar, John Lennon's collarless Beatles jacket, Jim Morrison's Cub Scout uniform, David Bowie's exaggerated 1970s fashions, Michael Jackson's sequined glove — you get the idea.

✔ As resplendent as any Loire Valley chateau, the massive 250-room Biltmore mansion and its gardens, crafts shops, and winery give a full picture of how the other half once lived. The Vanderbilts were American royalty, and with the help of architect Richard Morris Hunt and landscape designer Frederick Law Olmstead (who also designed New York's Central Park), created their own kingdom in the mountains of western North Carolina in the late 1800s. Today, for a price, anyone can tour the splendid **Biltmore Estate,** 1 Approach Rd., Asheville, North Carolina (☎ **800-624-1575;** www.biltmore.com).

✔ **Monticello** (☎ **434-984-9822;** www.monticello.org), the gracious home of our third president, Thomas Jefferson, along with its original furnishings, his gardens, and his grave, tells a great deal about the man and the statesman. The house is elegant but on a human scale, designed by Jefferson himself, who hated the 18th-century brick buildings of Williamsburg. Lewis and Clark brought back the moose and deer antlers in the entry hall from their expedition. Always a generous host, Jefferson was $100,000 in debt, a sum equivalent to a million dollars today, when he died. The house is located 3 miles southeast of Charlottesville, Virginia, on U.S. 53.

✔ **Vicksburg National Military Park,** 3201 Clay St., Vicksburg, Mississippi (☎ **601-636-0583;** www.nps.gov/vick), commemorates one of the most decisive battles of the Civil War. General Ulysses S. Grant and 50,000 men held the city under siege for 47 days. The national cemetery contains the graves of some 17,000 Union soldiers. A 16-mile auto tour around the park passes markers, monuments, and re-created breastworks. In the museum, you can see the gunboat *Cairo,* which was pulled up from the Yazoo River 100 years after it sank in 1862.

✔ Extremely popular with Old West aficionados, as well as kids of all ages, California's **Calico Ghost Town,** at the Calico exit off I-15 or I-40 east of Barstow (☎ 760-254-2122; www.calicotown.com), isn't a built-for-tourists ghost town that some people expect; instead, it's a real silver-mining town that thrived from 1881 to 1907 with a population of 3,500. Walter Knott (of Knott's Berry Farm fame), who worked in the mines as a youth, restored and preserved the town, which is operated today by the San Bernardino County Park System. Original and reconstructed buildings, including a house made of glass bottles, sometimes serve as a backdrop for staged gunfights and other Western shenanigans on weekends and in summer.

✔ If you're traveling with kids (or you have a sweet tooth of your own), you can't go wrong with a trip to the **Jelly Belly Candy Company,** 2400 N. Watney Way, Fairfield, California (☎ 707-428-2800; www.jellybelly.com), which offers our hands-down favorite of all the factory tours in the U.S. Here you can watch the candies being made on the assembly line and taste them at different stages, get free samples at the end of the tour, and buy low-price factory rejects called Belly Flops, which usually are two jelly beans that fused together.

Enjoying a Volunteer Vacation

"Working" vacations have become more and more popular over the last few years and numerous volunteer and study programs are available both in the U.S. and around the world. Volunteering can be a unique and rewarding way to spend your vacation time. Here are a few places to start:

✔ **Habitat for Humanity** (☎ 800-422-4828; www.habitat.org) gives you the chance to build or rehabilitate simple, decent houses with the help of the homeowner families. In addition to helping people create safe, affordable houses in communities all across the U.S., Habitat works in communities hit by natural disasters. You can also travel around the world building houses with Habitat.

✔ **Earthwatch Institute** (☎ 800-776-0188; www.earthwatch.org) organizes volunteers to go on research trips to help scientists collect data and conduct field experiments in a number of scientific fields and a wide range of settings. You can observe Alaskan fur seals, study climate change and caterpillars in New Orleans, or head farther afield — maybe documenting the traditional culture in China's Yulin area. The possibilities really are endless.

✔ **Global Volunteers** (☎ 800-487-1074; www.global volunteers.org) is a U.S.-based organization that offers a unique opportunity to travelers who've always wanted a Peace Corps–like experience but can't make a two-year commitment. Head to West Virginia and reno- vate homes or tutor children in coal-mining towns, serve the Blackfeet Nation in Montana, or even assist with healthcare in the African nation of Ghana.

Booking Your Trip, Saving Money, and Staying Safe

As you get older, it's natural to have some concerns about traveling. In this section, we give you tips that'll help you book a safe, relatively inexpensive, and worry-free vacation.

Finding the best rate on a room

When it comes to rates, the most common term is *rack rate*. The rack rate is the maximum rate that a resort or hotel charges for a room. It's the rate you get if you walk in off the street and ask for a room.

Always ask whether a lower rate or special package is available — it can't hurt, and you may at least end up with a free breakfast or spa service. If you're taking a vacation with your entire family or a group of friends, you may be able to get a group discount with hotels and some attractions. Call ahead to check.

Minimum-night stays, special promotions, and seasonal dis- counts can all go a long way toward bringing the rate down. Also, be sure to mention your membership in frequent-flier or rewards programs if you book with one of the larger hotel chains.

You'll likely get the best rate by booking your hotel as part of an air-hotel package, but in lieu of that, try contacting the local number of the hotel for your best chance of negotiating a good rate.

Surfing the Web for hotel deals

The Web is a great place to browse hotel options and also find good deals on rooms. Expedia.com offers a long list of special deals and *virtual tours* or photos of available rooms so you can see what you're paying for (a feature that helps counter the claims that the best rooms are often held back from bargain booking Web sites). Travelocity.com posts unvarnished customer reviews and ranks its properties according to the AAA rating system.

HotelChatter (`www.hotelchatter.com`) is a daily Webzine offering smart coverage and critiques of hotels worldwide. Go to TripAdvisor (`www.tripadvisor.com`) or HotelShark (`www.hotelshark.com`) for independent consumer reviews of hotels and resorts.

Many of these sites also allow you to book your room online from the comfort of your couch, and they've gone through great pains to ensure that your personal data and credit card numbers stay safe and secure. When making any online purchase, make sure the Web address starts with `https://` — this lets you know that the site is a secure one. Also, be sure to get a confirmation number and make a printout of any online booking transaction that you make, just in case you show up at the hotel and it doesn't have a record of your reservation.

Reserving the best room

Whether you book online or over the phone, make sure you ask lots of questions when you're making your reservation — doing so may result in your getting a better or cheaper room:

- ✔ **Ask if you can have a corner room.** They're often larger and quieter, with more windows and light, but for the same price as standard rooms.

- ✔ **Ask if the hotel is renovating.** If it is, request a room away from the construction.

> ✔ Ask for a room that has been recently renovated or refurbished.
>
> ✔ Ask about nonsmoking rooms and rooms with views.
>
> ✔ If you're a light sleeper, ask for a quiet room away from vending machines or ice machines, elevators, restaurants, bars, and discos.

If you aren't happy with your room when you arrive, ask for a different one. Most places will happily oblige.

Using your seniority

Being a senior entitles you to some terrific travel bargains. Mention the fact that you're a senior when you make your travel reservations. Although all the major U.S. airlines except America West have canceled their senior discount and coupon-book programs, many hotels still offer discounts for seniors. In most cities, people 60 and over qualify for reduced admission to theaters, museums, and other attractions, as well as discounted fares on public transportation.

Handling your money and dealing with emergencies

Traveler's checks are almost completely a thing of the past. Though you can still use them, your best bet is to carry two credit cards (so if one is declined for some reason, you have a backup). Credit cards are safe, provide a convenient record of your expenses, and generally offer good exchange rates.

If you need cash, your best bet is to use an ATM card; even with the international transaction fees, ATMs offer the best exchange rates. Avoid exchanging money at commercial exchange bureaus and hotels, which often have high fees.

 Before you leave home, head to your local copy shop with your wallet and passport, and make two photocopies of the front and back sides of everything. Write down the toll-free and direct-dial numbers of your credit card companies on the same piece of paper. Then leave a copy of everything with a friend or family member back home, and keep another copy of it somewhere safe with your luggage (but not in your wallet).

Many credit cards have direct-dial phone numbers that you can call collect, because toll-free numbers don't work abroad, so you'll need to have the direct-dial numbers handy in case of emergency. If this data isn't listed on the back of your card, go online or call your credit card provider before you hit the road to find out this important information.

When you arrive at your destination, keep your passport and a backup credit card in your hotel room safe to minimize the chances of loss or theft. If you'd rather have your passport and credit cards with you at all times, the safe is a great place to store a photocopy of your passport and credit cards.

If you discover that your wallet has been lost or stolen, contact all your credit card companies immediately, and file a report at the local police department. If you left home without having made photocopies of all your credit card information, call ☎ 800-555-1212 to get your issuing bank's toll-free number. For **American Express** cards call ☎ **800-992-3404;** outside the U.S., call collect 336-393-1111. If you need emergency cash, you can have money wired to you via **Western Union** (☎ **800-325-6000;** www.westernunion.com).

Losing your passport is not the end of the world, but you do need to replace a lost or stolen passport immediately. First, report it to the police. Then contact the nearest consulate or high commission office and begin to take the necessary steps to get a new one.